STAR WARS®

EMPIRE

VOLUME SEVEN: THE WRONG SIDE OF THE WAR

DARK HORSE BOOKS™

THESE STORIES TAKE PLACE
APPROXIMATELY EIGHT MONTHS AFTER
THE EVENTS IN Star Wars: A New Hope.

STAR WARS: Empire volume 7

This volume collects issues #35-40 of the
Dark Horse comic-book series
Star Wars: Empire.

Published by
Dark Horse Books
A division of Dark Horse Comics, Inc.
10956 SE Main Street
Milwaukie, OR 97222

DARKHORSE.COM
STARWARS.COM

To find a comics shop in your
area, call the Comic Shop
Locator Service toll-free
at 1-888-266-4226

First edition: January 2007
ISBN-10: 1-59307-709-2
ISBN-13: 978-1-59307-709-9

1 3 5 7 9 10 8 6 4 2

Printed in China

VOLUME SEVEN:
THE WRONG SIDE OF THE WAR

WRITERS WELLES HARTLEY
JOHN JACKSON MILLER

PENCILLERS DAVIDÉ FABBRI
BRIAN CHING

INKER CHRISTIAN DALLA VECCHIA

COLORISTS DAVIDÉ FABBRI
NEZITI DOMENICO
MICHAEL ATIYEH

LETTERER MICHAEL DAVID THOMAS

COVER ART BY DAVID MICHAEL BECK
AND BRAD ANDERSON

PUBLISHER
MIKE RICHARDSON

COLLECTION DESIGNER
SCOTT COOK

ART DIRECTOR
LIA RIBACCHI

ASSISTANT EDITOR
DAVE MARSHALL

ASSOCIATE EDITOR
JEREMY BARLOW

EDITOR
RANDY STRADLEY

SPECIAL THANKS TO
LELAND CHEE, SUE ROSTONI,
AND **AMY GARY** AT LUCAS LICENSING

MODEL OFFICER

Script JOHN JACKSON MILLER

Art BRIAN CHING

Colors MICHAEL ATIYEH

MEDIC...

...MED...

ALL OF THE REBELS ARE DEAD.

I EXPECTED NO LESS FROM *REPRISAL.*

I COMMEND YOUR GUNNERY CREW, CAPTAIN SANKARAN. ESPECIALLY YOUR TIMING...

...A KILL IS NEVER SO SATISFYING AS WHEN YOUR TARGET SEES IT COMING.

THANK YOU, COMMANDER DEMMINGS!

FROM THE PRISONER JORIN SOL, WE NOW KNOW HOW THE FLEET'S ESCAPE ALGORITHM WORKS. ALL WE NEED TO CALCULATE ITS *NEXT* DESTINATION IS TO KNOW WHERE IT IS *NOW*.

WE COULD BE POISED TO STRIKE A CRUSHING BLOW NEXT TIME THEY RUN -- IF YOU HADN'T WIPED OUT THE SCOUTS!

WELL. MY APOLOGIES, LORD VADER, FOR MY *OVER-* EFFICIENCY.

ORBITAL STRIKES ARE AN IMPRECISE BUSINESS. I'M AFRAID MY CREW TENDS TO ERR ON THE SIDE OF GREATER FIREPOWER.

BUT, IN MY CAREER, I HAVE OFTEN FOUND SURVIVORS ... *INCONVENIENT.* THEY'RE A MISTAKE I TRY TO AVOID.

ENOUGH! YOU MAY TAKE PRIDE IN YOUR PERFORMANCE, DEMMINGS, ONLY WHEN THAT PERFORMANCE SUITS *ME.*

A SECOND GROUP OF REBELS HAS BEEN DETECTED IN THIS SECTOR. IF YOU'RE THE MODEL OFFICER YOU CLAIM, YOU'LL SEE THEM INTO MY HANDS -- *ALIVE!*

YES, MY LORD.

OF COURSE.

RIGHT WHERE LORD VADER SAID THEY'D BE, SIR. THEY'RE RUNNING!

THEY'LL SEEK A LANE FOR THEIR HYPERSPACE JUMP. CUT THEM OFF AND PREPARE TO FIRE...

...PRECISION SHOTS. DISABLING -- OF COURSE.

STAR DESTROYER'S VEERING OFF!

I'M HEARTBROKEN! MAKE FOR THE POINT!

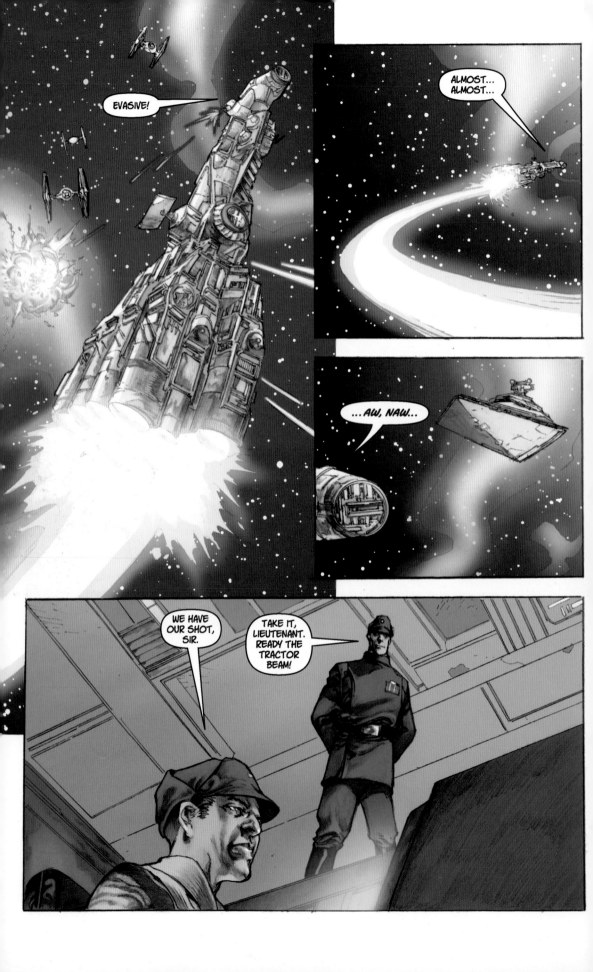

GASP! KAFF!

WH -- WHY --

BLOODLUST IS A VALUABLE TRAIT, CAPTAIN, BUT IT MUST ALWAYS DEFER TO THE PLANS OF THE EMPEROR.

FOLLOW ME.

LATER...

CREW OF THE *REPRISAL*...

...LORD VADER HAS SHOWN ME THE LOCATION OF A *THIRD* REBEL PATROL. THIS IS WHAT HAS BOUGHT US TO THE *EJOLUS* SYSTEM.

WE HAVE BEEN GIVEN ONE *FINAL CHANCE* TO REDEEM OURSELVES.

I KNOW... YOU WILL *ALL DO* YOUR DUTY...

WE HAVE IT, SIR!

A SINGLE OUTPOST -- NO INDICATION THEY'VE DETECTED US YET.

LOOKS TO BE A SMALL AGRARIAN SETTLEMENT, SIR.

AHEM. DON'T BE FOOLED, COMMANDER.

THE ALLIANCE IS GETTING BETTER AT HIDING THEIR DEFLECTOR SHIELDS. LOOK THERE, AT THE FRINGE OF THE SETTLEMENT.

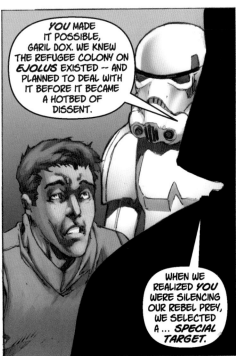

THE WRONG SIDE OF THE WAR

Script WELLES HARTLEY
Pencils DAVIDÉ FABBRI
Inks CHRISTIAN DALLA VECCHIA
Colors DAVIDÉ FABBRI
NEZITI DOMENICO

THE PLANET **JABIIM,** TWO WEEKS AFTER THE ARRIVAL OF **DARTH VADER** AND THE BEGINNING OF ORBITAL BOMBARDMENT.

BLUE THREE. APPROACH VECTOR LOCKED IN...

ANY ACADEMY PLEBE COULD SEE -- AFTER THE STAR DESTROYERS' TURBOLASERS FAILED TO PENETRATE THE TARGET FROM ORBIT --

-- THAT THE **ONLY** WAY THIS LAST REBEL STRONGHOLD WOULD BE TAKEN WAS FROM **THE GROUND.**

SO, OF COURSE, THE INFANTRY WAS ORDERED TO **STAND BY,** WHILE GOOD MACHINES --

-- AND GOOD PILOTS, WERE **WASTED** IN ANOTHER FUTILE ATTEMPT FROM ABOVE.

LIEUTENANT JANEK SUNBER HAS ARRIVED AT HIS DESTINATION WITH FEWER THAN HALF THE MEN WITH WHICH HE STARTED.

THE NECESSITY OF SUCCESS DICTATES THAT THEY WILL HAVE TO BE ENOUGH.

THE ARTILLERY SUPPORT, IF IT ARRIVES AT ALL, CAN DO LITTLE MORE THAN PROVIDE A TEMPORARY DISTRACTION FOR THEIR ENEMIES.

SET THOSE CHARGES -- WE DON'T HAVE MUCH TIME!

THE FIRST TIME SUNBER SAW ACTION, THE IMPERIAL POSITION WAS REVERSED. THEN IT WAS HIS OWN SMALL COMPANY DEFENDING AGAINST A LARGER ATTACKING FORCE.

THEN IT WAS HIS OWN TRAPS AND DEFENSES THAT REDUCED THE ATTACKERS' NUMBERS.

NOW IT IS IMPERIAL FLESH AND BLOOD THAT IS BEING HURLED AGAINST A DEFENDER'S BULWARKS.

BUT, IF ONE SITUATION IS PREFERABLE TO THE OTHER, IT DOES NOT OCCUR TO SUNBER.

HE AND HIS TROOPS HAVE THEIR ORDERS -- AND THEY MUST CARRY THEM OUT, OR DIE TRYING.

THROW DOWN YOUR WEAPONS!

IT ISN'T LONG BEFORE ALL OPPOSITION IS SUBDUED.

THEN COMES THE PART OF EVERY OPERATION FOR WHICH SUNBER STILL HAS NO STOMACH...

FORM TWO LINES! CHILDREN AND THE ELDERLY IN ONE, EVERYONE ELSE IN THE OTHER!

NO! NOT MY SON!

THEY ARE BRED PURELY FOR DUTY -- PLIABLE, PATIENT, AND TOUGH. THOUGH, SUNBER HAS HEARD THAT DURING THE CLONE WARS, THEY WERE EVEN *TOUGHER*.

ATTENTION ALL PERSONNEL --

-- STAND BY TO EXIT HYPERSPACE.

BUT THE PRISONERS TAKEN ON JABIIM ARE BEYOND ENVY.

WHAT DROVE THEM, SUNBER WONDERS, TO ATTEMPT A STAND AGAINST THE EMPIRE? WHAT COULD COMPEL SO MANY TO CHOOSE A COURSE THAT WOULD LEAD THEM TO AN ALMOST CERTAIN DEATH --

-- OR TO THEIR CURRENT FATE?

STRANGER STILL, ARE THE MOTIVES OF THEIR OTHER PRISONER...

...THE REBEL SPY -- JORIN SOL.

RUMOR HAS IT THAT SOL HAS ATTRACTED THE ATTENTION OF LORD VADER HIMSELF BECAUSE OF HIS KNOWLEDGE OF THE LOCATION OF THE REBEL FLEET.

WHAT KIND OF LIFE MUST THE YOUNG MAN HAVE HAD? WHAT COULD HAVE LED HIM TO CAST HIS FATE WITH THAT OF THE HOPELESS REBEL ALLIANCE?

BUT SUNBER REALIZES THAT HIS OWN DECISIONS HAVE LED HIM TO SITUATIONS WHICH HE COULD NOT HAVE ANTICIPATED.

SO MUCH OF A MAN'S LIFE IS DETERMINED BY CHOICES THAT SEEM OF LITTLE IMPORT AT THE TIME THEY ARE MADE...

MAYBE IT'S THE SAME FOR HIM...

HMM? WHAT'S THAT, LIEUTENANT?

UH, MY MEN ARE READY FOR LANDING, SIR --

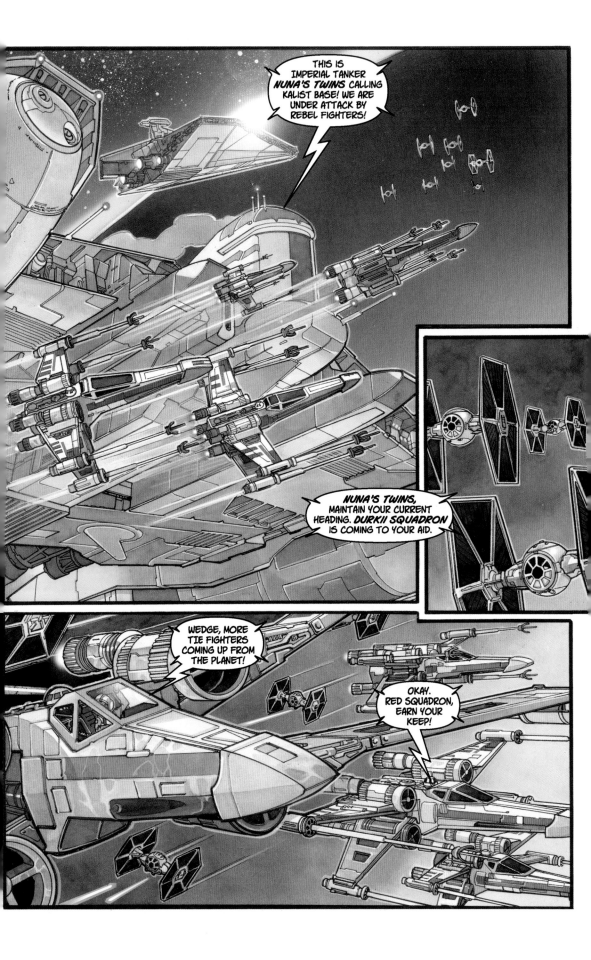

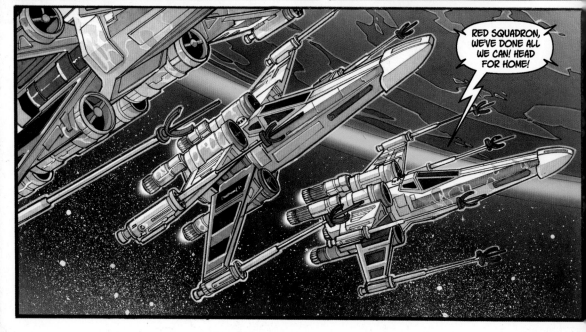

-- BUT AT LEAST IT WILL BRING NEW DUTIES WITH WHICH TO OCCUPY HIS TIME.

PRISONERS WILL FORM RANKS FOR DEBARKATION! ANYONE DISRUPTING THE OFF-LOADING PROCESS WILL BE SHOT!

OFFICERS -- KALIST BASE IS ON A STATE OF *HIGH ALERT* DUE TO THE REBEL ATTACK. PRISONERS WILL BE OFF-LOADED AT DOUBLE-TIME SPEED!

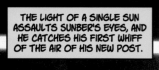

THE LIGHT OF A SINGLE SUN ASSAULTS SUNBER'S EYES, AND HE CATCHES HIS FIRST WHIFF OF THE AIR OF HIS NEW POST.

IT IS DRIER AND CLEANER THAN THE FETID AIR OF JABIIM, BUT WITHOUT THE ACRID BITE HE REMEMBERS FROM HIS HOMEWORLD. MORE SAND HERE, LESS DUST.

THE PRISONER SOL IS TO BE HANDED OVER TO THE MUCH-WHISPERED-ABOUT *ANALYSIS BUREAU* OF IMPERIAL INTELLIGENCE.

WHATEVER FATE AWAITS THE JABIIMI PRISONERS, SUNBER KNOWS IT WILL BE A KINDER ONE THAN JORIN SOL'S.

AND THAT IS THE LAST TIME HE WILL THINK OF SOL FOR SEVERAL DAYS. FOR NOW, A NEW ASSIGNMENT LIES AHEAD, AND DUTY CALLS.

DUTY -- THE MISTRESS TO WHOM SUNBER HAS WILLINGLY CHAINED HIMSELF. THOUGH DEMANDING AND UNFORGIVING, SHE IS ALWAYS CONSISTENT. AND IN THAT CERTAINTY, THERE IS A CERTAIN KIND OF COMFORT.

FOR DUTY NEVER ASKS FOR MORE THAN HER SUITORS CAN GIVE. ALL SHE EVER ASKS FOR IS ... ALL.

ALL RIGHT, THEN. THE TRANSPORT IS SAFELY DOWN. WHAT ABOUT THIS TANKER --?

NUNA'S TWINS. IT WAS DUE HERE TWO DAYS AGO, SIR. ROUTINE SUPPLY RUN, BUT IT SHOULD BE ACCOMPANIED BY --

AN ESCORT FRIGATE. RIGHT.

HAVE CAPTAIN JODEEN AND HIS MEN SURROUND THAT TANKER. DON'T LET IT COME ANY CLOSER.

TANKER NUNA'S TWINS, STAND TO. YOU WILL HOLD YOUR CURRENT POSITION, ON ORDERS FROM GENERAL NOILS.

CAPTAIN HARRAN, HERE. THIS SHOW OF FORCE IS UNNECESSARY, GENERAL.

I'LL BE THE JUDGE OF THAT, CAPTAIN. BUT FIRST --

CONFINED TO SHIP? THIS IS UNHEARD OF, GENERAL!

I BELIEVE THE DESTRUCTION OF ONE OF THE EMPEROR'S FRIGATES AND A REBEL ATTACK UPON A HEAVILY DEFENDED IMPERIAL BASE *WARRANTS* IT, CAPTAIN.

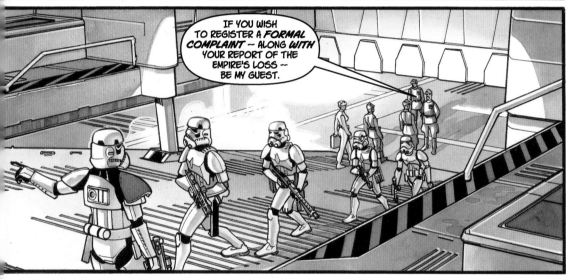

IF YOU WISH TO REGISTER A *FORMAL COMPLAINT* -- ALONG *WITH* YOUR REPORT OF THE EMPIRE'S LOSS -- BE MY GUEST.

MY APOLOGIES, SIR. PLEASE UNDERSTAND THAT MY CREW AND I ARE EXHAUSTED. WE JUST SPENT FORTY-EIGHT HOURS TRYING TO SHAKE THOSE REBELS.

IF IT WASN'T FOR LIEUTENANT JUNDLAND'S QUICK THINKING --

NO APOLOGIES ARE NECESSARY, CAPTAIN. THIS REBELLION TRIES US ALL.

EVERY DECISION HAS ITS CONSEQUENCES.

SOME ARE JUST MORE **CONSEQUENTIAL** THAN OTHERS.

AND, ALL TOO OFTEN, CONSEQUENCES BEAR THE BITTER FRUIT OF **REGRET**.

HOW MANY OF HIS PAST DECISIONS DOES **JORIN SOL** REGRET?

CERTAINLY, HE MUST REGRET HIS DECISION TO JOIN SENATOR ORGANA'S PARTY ON HER MISSION TO JABIIM. PROBABLY, HE REGRETS HIS DECISION TO EVER CAST HIS LOT WITH THE REBEL ALLIANCE.

BUT WHAT ELSE? HOW FAR BACK DO HIS REGRETS STRETCH?

DOES HE REGRET HIS DECISION TO SPECIALIZE IN MATHEMATICS?

DOES HE REGRET THE BLESSING OF A BRILLIANT MIND, WHICH LED HIM TO HIS SPECIALTY? DOES HE REGRET HIS OWN **BIRTH**?

PLEASE! **STOP!** THIS ISN'T NECESSARY!

IT-0, STOP.

STOPPING.

AND WHAT IS IT, JORIN, THAT MAKES YOU THINK THIS IS *UNNECESSARY?*

YOU DON'T HAVE TO HURT ME. I ALREADY TOLD DARTH -- UH, L-LORD VADER EVERYTHING!

I TOLD HIM ALL ABOUT THE ALLIANCE "SCRAMBLE CODE" -- I GAVE HIM THE LOGARITHM I DEVELOPED FOR THE --

OH, JORIN, YOU SILLY BOY.

I KNOW ALL THAT. BUT THIS ISN'T ABOUT WHAT YOU *KNOW*... THIS IS ABOUT WHAT YOU'LL *DO* -- FOR *ME*.

IT-0, RESUME THE SESSION.

RESUMING INTERROGATION.

NOOO!

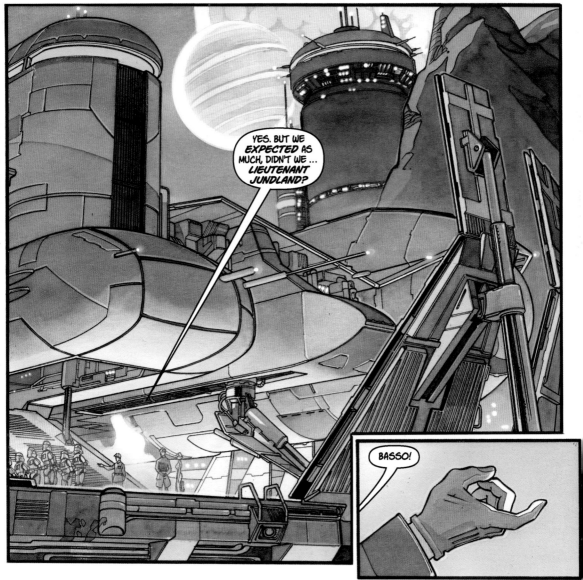

OKAY, LET'S GET THIS DECK CLEARED BEFORE SOMEBODY SEES. ON THE DOUBLE!

DEENA...?

THE CAPTAIN'S CALLED A FINAL BRIEFING.

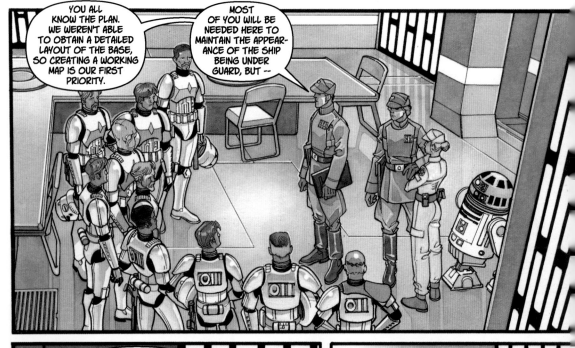

YOU ALL KNOW THE PLAN. WE WEREN'T ABLE TO OBTAIN A DETAILED LAYOUT OF THE BASE, SO CREATING A WORKING MAP IS OUR FIRST PRIORITY.

MOST OF YOU WILL BE NEEDED HERE TO MAINTAIN THE APPEARANCE OF THE SHIP BEING UNDER GUARD, BUT --

-- BASSO, YOU AND ABLE ARE GOING IN. KEEP TRACK OF WHERE YOU PUT THE DIVERSIONARIES.

SURE THING, CAP.

MOUSE, YOU'RE GOING AFTER THE "PRIZE." ANY PROBLEMS?

THE HELMET IS TOO SMALL, AN' THE GLOVES ARE TOO SHORT. NC PROBLEMS, SIR.

OKAY, PEOPLE, WE HAVE JUST OVER FORTY-EIGHT HOURS. GO TO WORK.

SKYWALKER, GET THAT ARTOO UNIT OF YOURS BUSY ON THOSE FUEL PUMPS!

BEEWOOP!

AFTER IT WAS DETERMINED THAT NO FURTHER REBEL ATTACKS WERE IMMINENT, LT. JANEK SUNBER SAW TO IT THAT HIS REMAINING TROOPERS WERE ASSIGNED TO A NEW COMPANY --

-- THEN FOUND AN EMPTY BUNK FOR HIMSELF IN THE JUNIOR OFFICERS' BARRACKS.

HE HAD BEEN ISSUED A NEW KIT. HIS BELONGINGS HAD BEEN LISTED AS "LOST IN TRANSIT" FROM JABIIM.

IT WAS NOT THE FIRST TIME.

JANEK SUNBER LEARNED A LONG TIME AGO TO FORGO ATTACHMENT TO PERSONAL ITEMS OR MEMENTOS.

LIFE IN THE INFANTRY IS LIVED BY THE INFANTRY'S RULES...

...AND RULE NUMBER ONE, AT HOME OR IN THE FIELD -- YOU FIGHT FOR EVERY CENTIMETER...

PARK YOUR CARCASS IN ANOTHER ROOM! THIS ONE'S MINE!

HEY, MEAT!

...AND YOU DEFEND IT AGAINST ALL ENEMIES.

REALLY? I WAS UNDER THE IMPRESSION THAT IT BELONGED TO THE GALACTIC EMPIRE.

HEY! THE NEW GUY IS TRYING TO MOVE INTO CLYNN'S ROOM!

HE'S WHAT?

OH, THIS'LL BE GOOD.

WHAT'S THE STORY ON THE NEW GUY?

HE CAME IN FROM JABIIM, SO HE'S SEEN SOME ACTION.

NOT MUCH, I BET. I HEARD THEY WERE JUST ROUNDING UP SLAVES.

"CLYNN WILL CRUSH HIM."

CAPTAIN ON DECK!

SUNBER! CLYNN!

WHAT'S THE MEANING OF THIS?

CLYNN, YOU'VE BEEN WARNED ABOUT FIGHTING. DO YOU WANT TO END UP IN THE STOCKADE?!

NO, SIR.

THEN YOU'LL TAKE ON *EXTRA DUTIES.* YOU TWO ARE SUPERVISING THE NEXT TWO SHIFTS -- *TOGETHER.*

THIS IS YOUR LAST WARNING, CLYNN.

AND YOU, SUNBER -- THIS IS NO WAY TO BEGIN A NEW ASSIGNMENT. MAYBE THIS IS THE WAY YOU HANDLED DISAGREEMENTS AT YOUR *PREVIOUS* POST...

...BUT YOU'RE NOT ON *MARIDUN* ANYMORE.

MARIDUN?!

AH, CAPTAIN HARRAN! MY APOLOGIES TO YOU AND YOUR CREW FOR THE MISUNDERSTANDING LAST NIGHT.

THE STRAIN OF RUNNING THIS BASE AND TRYING TO CONDUCT A WAR AGAINST AN ENEMY WHO REFUSES TO STAND AND FIGHT HAS TAKEN ITS TOLL ON MY MANNERS, I'M AFRAID.

NONSENSE, GENERAL. IT'S QUITE UNDERSTANDABLE, GIVEN THE CIRCUMSTANCES.

THE COWARDLY HIT AND RUN TACTICS USED BY THE REBELLION AREN'T EXACTLY WHAT WE WERE TRAINED FOR AT THE ACADEMY.

I DARE SAY!

FROM THE SOUNDS OF IT, YOU AND YOUR SHIP WERE IN THE *THICK* OF IT -- AND WITH A *LADY* ON BOARD, TOO.

A LADY, YES, BUT AN *IMPERIAL OFFICER* FIRST. AM I RIGHT?

LIEUTENANT SHAN, CAPTAIN -- ?

ROSHUIR. A TANKER IS AN UNUSUAL PLACE FOR A *SCIENCE OFFICER*, ISN'T IT?

I HAVE ORDERS TO MONITOR FUEL CONSUMPTION AT IMPERIAL BASES. BORING, ROUTINE WORK --

-- BUT I GO WHERE THE EMPIRE SENDS ME, CAPTAIN.

THEN WE HERE ON KALIST VI SHALL COUNT OURSELVES FORTUNATE.

≀ AHEM ≀ YES ... WELL, I ASKED THE CAPTAIN TO JOIN US IN THE HOPES THAT HE COULD PREPARE AN ACTION AGAINST THE REBELS WHO ATTACKED YOUR SHIP.

IF YOU COULD PINPOINT THE LOCATION WHERE YOU FIRST ENCOUNTERED THE REBELS...

CERTAINLY. LIEUTENANT JUNDLAND...

YES, SIR. WE FIRST SPOTTED THE REBELS *HERE* --

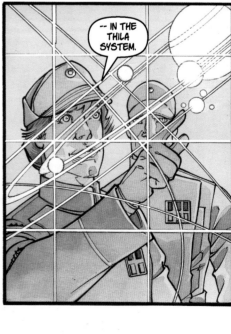

-- IN THE THILA SYSTEM.

THILA. THERE WERE *RUMORS* OF A REBEL BASE THERE, BUT NOTHING HAS BEEN REPORTED FOR SOME TIME NOW.

IT'S POSSIBLE THEY'RE PLANNING A *NEW* OFFENSIVE...

THAT'S WHAT *YOU* HAVE TO FIND OUT.

PERHAPS *I* CAN *ASSIST* CAPTAIN ROSHUIR, GENERAL.

DURING MY FINAL TRAINING, I WAS PART OF A GEOGRAPHIC SURVEY OF THE THILA SYSTEM.

I'M SURE THAT IF THE CAPTAIN AND I COMBINE OUR ... AREAS OF EXPERTISE ... WE COULD LOCATE THE MOST LIKELY HIDING PLACE FOR A REBEL BASE.

I THINK THAT'S AN *EXCELLENT* IDEA, SIR.

VERY WELL.

IF YOU NEED ME, GENERAL, I'LL BE IN THE CARTOGRAPHY SECTION.

THIS WAY, LIEUTENANT...

THIS IS THE MAIN WORKSHOP. THE SLAVES WORK, THE STORMIES WATCH THE SLAVES, AND WE WATCH THE STORMIES.

THIS IS WHERE YOU'LL SPEND MOST OF YOUR TIME -- UNLESS WE GET SENT ON A MISSION.

DO WE GET SENT ON MANY MISSIONS?

NOT THAT MANY. DON'T WORRY --

OH, *I* GET IT. YOU GOT A *TASTE* FOR *ACTION* ON MARIDUN.

NO, IT'S NOT THAT. I JUST...

IT'S THE SLAVES. I DIDN'T EXPECT HUMANS --

MARIDUN! WHAT WAS IT LIKE? *HOLONET NEWS* SAID YOUR COMPANY DEFEATED HORDES OF MONSTER ALIENS WITH ONLY FIVE MEN IN THE END.

MORE LIKE *TWENTY*-FIVE. AND THE ALIENS -- THE *AMANIN* -- CALLED A TRUCE. I THINK THEY WERE ONLY TESTING OUR RESOLVE...

WELL, I HEARD IT WAS A GREAT DAY FOR THE EMPIRE. YOU GUYS WERE *HEROES*, SUNBER. YOU REALLY GAVE THE REBELS SOMETHING TO THINK ABOUT.

I BET THEY GAVE YOU A MEDAL, HUH?

THEY LET ME KEEP MY LIEUTENANT'S PATCH...

LOOK, CLYNN, I DON'T KNOW HOW MUCH ACTION YOU'VE SEEN --

I'VE SEEN MY SHARE, BUT NOTHING LIKE YOU!

IT DOESN'T *FEEL* HEROIC. MEN DIE...

...*TOO MANY* MEN. IF I'D DONE THINGS DIFFERENTLY -- IF I'D BEEN *SMARTER* -- MAYBE MORE OF MY MEN WOULD HAVE SURVIVED.

YOU SURE DON'T TALK LIKE A HERO.

YOU GO THROUGH LIFE WORRYING ABOUT WHAT YOU *SHOULD* HAVE DONE, PRETTY SOON YOU'LL BE SO FULL OF DOUBT AND QUESTIONS YOU WON'T BE ABLE TO DO THE *NEXT* THING.

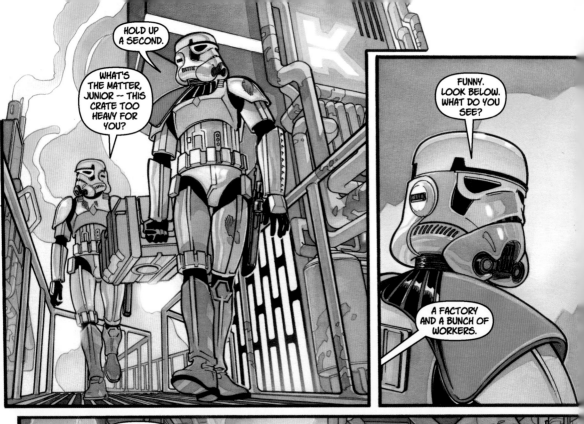

VERY WELL.

THOUGH I SHOULD WARN YOU -- STOPPING NOW WILL ONLY MAKE IT *HARDER* ON YOU WHEN WE *RESUME*...

...AND WE *WILL* RESUME. *SOON.* I WANT TO BE SURE I CAN TRUST YOUR *PROMISES.*

WE HAVE WHAT WE NEED, ZUUD. DON'T PUSH HIM TOO FAR.

I'M AWARE OF HIS LIMITS. I WANT TO BE CERTAIN.

LET'S MAKE *FULL USE* OF JORIN SOL --

-- IN THE TIME WE HAVE LEFT.

SHIFT'S OVER. TIME FOR SOME FUN.

I DON'T KNOW, CLYNN...

...I JUST PULLED TWO BACK-TO-BACK SHIFTS --

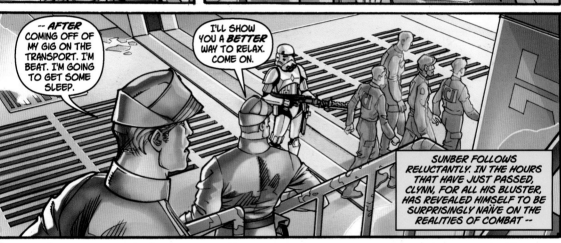

-- AFTER COMING OFF OF MY GIG ON THE TRANSPORT. I'M BEAT. I'M GOING TO GET SOME SLEEP.

I'LL SHOW YOU A BETTER WAY TO RELAX. COME ON.

SUNBER FOLLOWS RELUCTANTLY. IN THE HOURS THAT HAVE JUST PASSED, CLYNN, FOR ALL HIS BLUSTER, HAS REVEALED HIMSELF TO BE SURPRISINGLY NAÏVE ON THE REALITIES OF COMBAT --

-- BUT MORE PRACTICED THAN HE IS IN THE POLITICS OF MILITARY BUREAUCRACY.

HE DECIDES TO FOLLOW THE LEAD OF HIS NEW "FRIEND."

THIS LEADS TO THE WORKERS' QUARTERS...

SHOOT ANY OF THE PRISONERS WHO ATTEMPT TO FOLLOW ME.

YES, SIR.

STOP! WHAT ARE YOU DOING?

WHAT'S WITH YOU, SUNBER?

THIS IS ONE OF THE PERKS OF BEING ON THE WINNING SIDE!

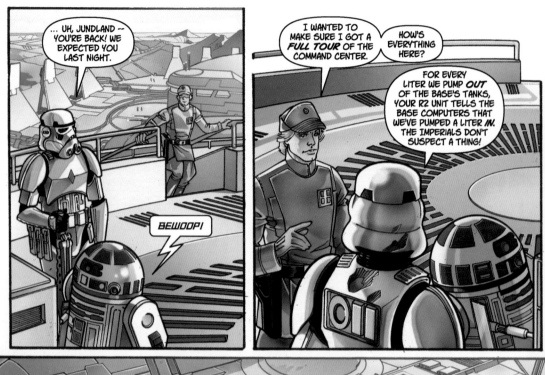

...GETTING EVERYONE OUT WOULD REQUIRE --

A *MASSIVE AIRLIFT* AND A *LARGER DIVERSION* THAN OUR LITTLE TEAM CAN PROVIDE. FORGET IT, LUKE. WE COULD *NEVER* MAKE IT WORK.

SIR, I RESPECTFULLY DISAGREE. IF THE IMPERIAL TRANSPORT IS STILL HERE WHEN --

YES! WE *COULD* DO IT.

BUT WE'D NEED PERFECT TIMING. IF WE COULD GET A MESSAGE TO THE REBEL FLEET --

OUT OF THE QUESTION! *ANY* TRANSMISSION WOULD BE PICKED UP BY THE IMPERIALS.

WE DON'T *NEED* TO CONTACT THEM. CAPTAIN ANTILLES AND HIS BOYS ARE COMING ANYWAY --

DO YOU REALIZE WHAT YOU'RE SUGGESTING? THINK OF WHAT IT COULD MEAN FOR THE FLEET IF WE FAIL TO RESCUE JORIN SOL -- OR IF WE DON'T COME BACK WITH THIS FUEL!

THINK OF WHAT IT *WILL* MEAN FOR THE SLAVES IF WE DO NOTHING. MY MISSION ON RALLTIIR LEFT ME *NO CHOICE* BUT TO LEAVE MY OWN PEOPLE BEHIND -- AND THEY WERE *SLAUGHTERED* BY THE EMPIRE.

I CAN'T TURN MY BACK ON INNOCENT CAPTIVES AGAIN. I *WON'T*, SIR.

ALL RIGHT. LUKE, SERGEANT, PUT TOGETHER A PLAN.

IF WE'RE GOING TO RISK EVERYTHING, WE SHOULD AT LEAST HAVE A PLAN.

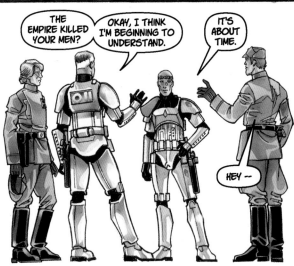

THE EMPIRE KILLED YOUR MEN?

OKAY, I THINK I'M BEGINNING TO UNDERSTAND.

IT'S ABOUT TIME.

HEY --

-- WHERE'S DEENA? SHE SHOULD HAVE BEEN BACK HOURS AGO!

NO. IT WOULD BE PRESUMPTUOUS OF ME. PERHAPS WHEN I RETURN.

"RETURN"?

YES, TOMORROW, PERHAPS -- THE DAY AFTER AT THE LATEST.

LIKE I SAID, THE INFORMATION YOU PROVIDED HAS GIVEN ME A GREAT OPPORTUNITY! I'VE BEEN CHOSEN TO LEAD THE ATTACK ON THE REBEL BASE ON THILA!

IF THE BASE IS WHERE YOU PREDICT, I'LL SOON HAVE A COMMANDER'S CODE CYLINDER!

BUT, KALE -- IT COULD BE DANGEROUS. THE REBELS MIGHT ANTICIPATE AN ATTACK...

...THERE MIGHT BE BOOBY TRAPS, OR --

HUSH. YOUR CONCERNS ARE UNFOUNDED. WHAT HOPE DO THE REBELS HAVE AGAINST TRAINED IMPERIAL TROOPS?

WAIT FOR ME, DEENA. I'LL RETURN AS QUICKLY AS I CAN!

WHAT HAVE I DONE?

SUNBER WAS CERTAIN THAT, AFTER THE INCIDENT WITH CLYNN, HE WOULD NOT BE ABLE TO SLEEP...

...WHICH IS WHY HE WAS SO SURPRISED TO FIND HIMSELF WAKING FROM IT.

ON THE DOUBLE! MOVE IT!

"B" COMPANY -- SEE TO YOUR MEN!

"C" COMPANY -- ISSUE SPECIAL WEAPONS PACKAGES!

THIS IS NOT A DRILL!

CAPTAIN ROSHUIR...

"TROOPERS ARE BEING SENT OFF ON A MISSION..."

...IT WON'T BE LONG NOW.

I HOPE YOU'RE RIGHT -- THAT SOL IS READY.

DEENA! UH ... LIEUTENANT SHAN...

...OR THAT IT DOESN'T EXIST AT ALL.

A FRIEND WILL EXPECT A SMILE OF RECOGNITION -- AN ACKNOWLEDGEMENT THAT, WHEN FACED TOGETHER, THE CURRENT SITUATION IS NOT SO TOUGH...

I'M GLAD I FOUND YOU! CAPTAIN HARRAN WAS GETTING WORRIED. WE ALL WERE.

ESPECIALLY WHEN THAT FRIEND IS ONE IN WHOM YEARS OF TRUST HAVE BEEN INVESTED...

WE SHOULD GET BACK TO THE SHIP -- GIVE THE CAPTAIN A FULL REPORT.

...WHEN THAT FRIEND IS FROM THE SAME GUILELESS FARMBOY STOCK AS ONESELF.

LUKE -- ?

LUKE SKYWALKER?

?

WAKE UP, SOL!

WHAP!

THERE WILL BE NO REST FOR YOU UNTIL I AM SATISFIED WITH YOUR CHOICE.

CHOOSE WISELY, AND THE PAIN WILL END AND YOU CAN SLEEP. OTHERWISE, WE WILL SEND YOU BACK TO LORD VADER!

NO!

NO...

NO. NO -- *WE* DON'T WANT THAT, EITHER, JORIN. BUT WE *MUST* HAVE YOUR DECISION --

"-- AND QUICKLY. THERE'S NOT MUCH TIME LEFT NOW."

WE'VE LESS THAN ELEVEN HOURS, CAPTAIN!

AND -- SOMEHOW -- IN THAT TIME WE HAVE TO FINISH PLANTING OUR EXPLOSIVES, TAKE ON THE REST OF THE FUEL, BE IN POSITION TO SPRING SOL, AND -- NOW -- RESCUE HUNDREDS OF PRISONERS, AS WELL!

DID YOU SUPPOSE THAT YOU WERE CHOSEN FOR THIS MISSION, BASSO, BECAUSE IT WOULD BE EASY?

WE HAVE GIVEN OUR WORD TO THE REBEL ALLIANCE TO RESCUE JORIN SOL, OR DIE TRYING. AS FOR THE OTHER PRISONERS --

-- WELL, WE CAN HARDLY TURN OUR BACKS ON SO MANY OF OUR FELLOW SENTIENTS, CAN WE?

BUT THE IMPERIALS CAN'T KILL US MORE THAN ONCE.

I WILL PLANT THE LAST OF THE EXPLOSIVES.

THANK YOU, MOUSE. JUST MAKE SURE YOU'RE BACK HERE BEFORE THE DIVERSIONARY FORCE ARRIVES.

MY APOLOGIES, CAPTAIN. YOU KNOW I'M NOT WORRIED ABOUT MY OWN SAFETY...

...IT'S THE *WHOLE* MISSION -- AND WHAT IT'S *BECOME.* WE'RE RISKING A LOT MORE THAN OUR OWN LIVES.

I *TRIED* TO WARN YOU ABOUT MAKING THE SLAVES A PART OF THIS, SARGE --

THAT'S ENOUGH, TROOPER ABLE. THE DECISION HAS BEEN MADE, AND IT'S TOO LATE TO BACK OUT NOW -- THOUGH I WISH WE COULD INFORM ALLIANCE H.Q. ABOUT THE CHANGE IN PLANS WITHOUT TIPPING-OFF THE IMPERIALS.

STILL, AS LONG AS WE HAVE THE ELEMENT OF SURPRISE ON OUR SIDE, THERE'S REASON TO BELIEVE WE CAN SUCCEED.

I'D BE MORE CONFIDENT IF I KNEW WHERE SHAN AND SKYWALKER WERE --

I'M RIGHT HERE, BUT --

-- LUKE RAN INTO SOMEBODY HE KNEW. AN IMPERIAL LIEUTENANT FROM *TATOOINE...*

I -- I DIDN'T KNOW.

WHAT HAPPENED?

HE WAS SHOT DOWN ... BY AN ENEMY FIGHTER. IT HAPPENED ABOVE YAVIN FOUR...

I *HEARD* ABOUT THAT ACTION! SOMETHING BIG. THE HIGHER-UPS WON'T TALK ABOUT IT. SOME KIND OF NEW *SPACE STATION*, OR SOMETHING.

YEAH, SOMETHING LIKE THAT. THE ALLIANCE DESTROYED IT -- A LUCKY SHOT. BUT BIGGS DIDN'T LIVE TO SEE IT. HE WAS KILLED SAVING MY LIFE.

HE WENT OUT A HERO.

YES...

LOOK, *TANK*...

HA! "TANK."

NOBODY CALLS ME THAT ANY MORE. IT'S BEEN A LONG TIME SINCE I WAS THE BIGGEST. IN FACT --

-- THERE'S ANOTHER LIEUTENANT IN MY BATTALION, A GUY NAMED CLYNN, WHO'S A GOOD HEAD TALLER THAN I AM, AND BUILT LIKE A DREADNAUGHT...

...HE TRIED TO BULLY ME ... AND ... AND HE TRIED TO MAKE ONE OF THE WOMEN PRISONERS, UH, TRIED TO MAKE HER...

IT'S STUPID, BUT I NEVER THOUGHT ABOUT IT BEFORE I JOINED THE SERVICE. I DIDN'T KNOW...

...THE EMPIRE HAS SLAVES -- HUMANS. AND NOT JUST PRISONERS OF WAR. I NEVER THOUGHT ABOUT IT.

MY GRANDFATHER WAS A SLAVE, YOU KNOW. I CAN'T IMAGINE WHAT HE'D SAY IF HE COULD SEE ME NOW...

TANK ... JANEK, WHAT DO YOU THINK ABOUT BEING IN THE EMPEROR'S SERVICE?

WHAT DO YOU DO WHEN YOUR ORDERS CALL FOR YOU TO DO SOMETHING THAT YOU KNOW ISN'T RIGHT?

THILA.

LIEUTENANT CLYNN, REPORT.

IT'S A BASE, ALL RIGHT -- OR IT WAS...

...BUT IT LOOKS *DESERTED*, NOW.

FIGURES...

WE'RE FORMING UP SQUADS TO SEARCH THE TUNNELS.

CARRY ON, LT. CLYNN. KEEP AN EYE OUT FOR ANYTHING THAT WILL BE OF INTEREST TO INTEL.

COPY.

BEEP! BEEP! BEWOOP!

WHAT'S WRONG WITH HIM?

STEADY, LITTLE FELLA. YOU COME UNPLUGGED NOW, AND THE IMPERIALS WILL DISCOVER THAT WE'VE *DRAINED* THEIR FUEL TANKS INSTEAD OF FILLING THEM.

CAN YOU SEE WHAT'S GOTTEN HIM SO EXCITED, BASSO?

UH, YEAH --

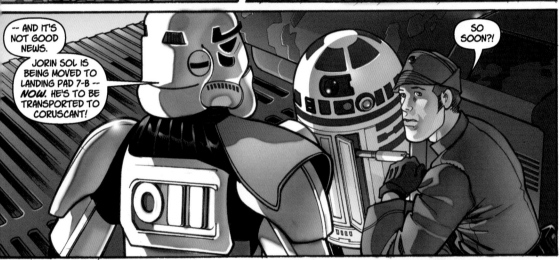

-- AND IT'S NOT GOOD NEWS.

JORIN SOL IS BEING MOVED TO LANDING PAD 7-B -- *NOW*. HE'S TO BE TRANSPORTED TO CORUSCANT!

SO SOON?!

ALL RIGHT -- WE GO *NOW!* THEY'RE MOVING OUR TARGET FROM HIS CELL TO *LANDING PAD 7-B.* YOU'VE GOT TO INTERCEPT HIM *BEFORE* HE REACHES HIS DESTINATION!

CAPTAIN, WE'RE NOT *READY!* THE STRIKE FORCE WON'T LAUNCH FOR HOURS, YET --

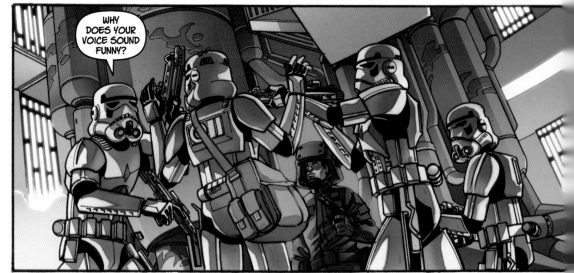

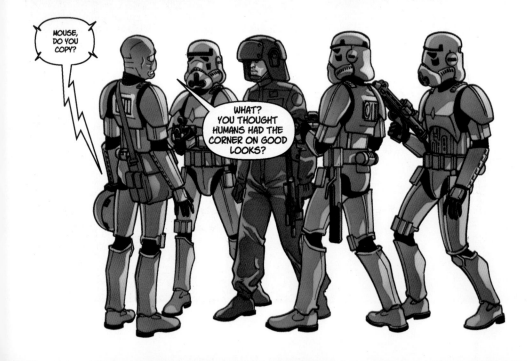

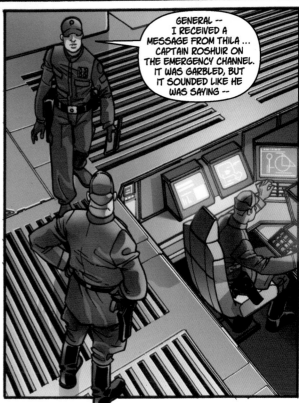

"-- THERE ARE *REBEL AGENTS* HERE ON THE BASE!"

YOU KNOW, LUKE, I WOULD NEVER MENTION THIS TO ANYBODY ELSE -- BUT SOMETIMES I THINK THE EMPIRE...

NO, NEVER MIND...

TANK, IT'S *ME.* YOU CAN TELL ME *ANYTHING.*

BELIEVE ME, I HAVE MY *OWN* DOUBTS ABOUT THE EMPIRE!

REALLY?

THAT DOESN'T *SOUND* LIKE THE KID I REMEMBER. NO HALF-MEASURES WITH YOU. YOU LED WITH YOUR HEART.

IF YOU DID SOMETHING, YOU DID IT ALL THE WAY.

YOU'RE NOT GETTING OLD AND CYNICAL ON ME, ARE YOU?

WHEN DID *YOU* GET SO BY-THE-BOOK?

YOU WERE ALWAYS THE FIRST ONE TO BEND -- OR *BREAK* -- THE RULES.

YEAH. WELL, I LEARNED THE *HARD WAY* THAT YOU CAN'T DO THAT IN THE INFANTRY -- NOT IF YOU WANT TO GET OUT OF THE TRENCHES.

AND I SAW HOW MUCH GOOD ORDER AND DISCIPLINE DID ME. I FIGURE IT'S GOT TO BE GOOD FOR THE REST OF THE GALAXY.

EVEN IF IT MEANS TURNING INNOCENT PEOPLE INTO SLAVES? EVEN IF IT MEANS *KILLING* THEM?

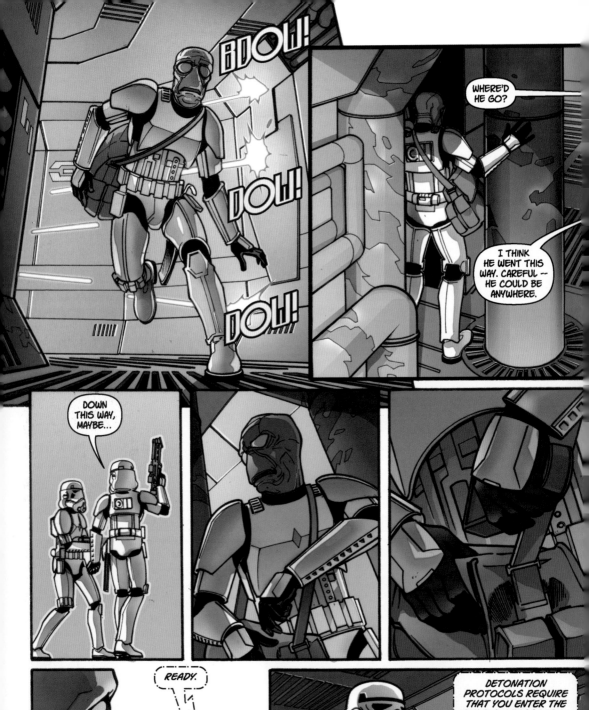

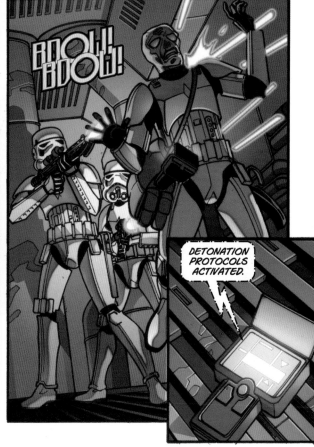

BOOOH!

YOU --!

KRAK!

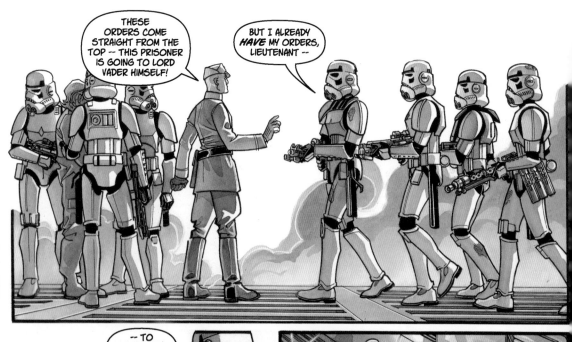

THESE ORDERS COME STRAIGHT FROM THE TOP -- THIS PRISONER IS GOING TO LORD VADER HIMSELF!

BUT I ALREADY *HAVE* MY ORDERS, LIEUTENANT --

-- TO *RELIEVE* YOU OF YOUR PRISONER.

BDOW!

BDOW!

DOW!

DOW!

IS SOL ALL RIGHT? OKAY --

-- DITCH THE HELMETS. WE DON'T WANT TO BE SHOT BY OUR OWN TROOPS.

JANEK SUNBER WAKES WITH THE TASTE OF BLOOD IN HIS MOUTH. THE SENSATION SURPRISES HIM, AS IT SEEMS UNCONNECTED WITH ANY MEMORY OF WHY THAT WOULD BE.

BUT THE MEMORIES ARRIVE, AND WHEN THEY DO, HE WISHES IT WERE OTHERWISE.

BETRAYED.

BY HIS BOYHOOD FRIEND. BY LUKE SKYWALKER.

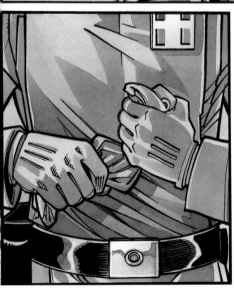

PRISONER DETAIL, THIS IS LIEUTENANT SUNBER! DO YOU READ ME?

REBELS ARE IN THE BASE. REPEAT -- REBELS ARE IN THE BASE!

VVVNNNN!

LOOK, I *CAN* SAVE YOU -- BUT YOU HAVE TO COME WITH ME *NOW!*

BLAST DOORS ARE SEALED. WE'RE CUT OFF FROM THE TANKER.

LOOKS LIKE THIS MISSION'S OVER, SARGE.

WE'RE NOT FINISHED YET, ABLE.

CAPTAIN! OUR PATH TO YOUR LOCATION IS BLOCKED. WE'RE GOING TO TRY ANOTHER WAY.

ANOTHER WAY? *WHAT* OTHER WAY?!

WE'LL HOOK UP WITH SKYWALKER. HE COULD PROBABLY USE THE HELP. SEE YOU BACK AT THE FLEET, CAPTAIN.

BASSO ... UH, ALL RIGHT. GOOD LUCK.

DEENA, GET ON THE SHIP. WE'RE GOING -- NOW.

HEAR THAT, ARTOO? THERE'S NO TIME FOR YOU TO FIND LUKE. YOU *HAVE* TO COME WITH US.

THERE! SET US DOWN CLOSE TO THAT TANKER!

NO BACKTALK! GO LOCK IN OUR COURSE!

BEEYOOP!

?

I NEED ANYBODY WITH PILOTING OR NAVI-GATION SKILLS ON THE BRIDGE!

HURRY! WE DON'T HAVE MUCH TIME.

LUKE!

GOING SOMEWHERE, FRIEND?

PLANNING ON LEAVING WITHOUT SAYING "GOOD-BYE"? OR WERE YOU HOPING I'D DIE IN THE BOMBARDMENT?

LET THEM GO. THEY'RE PRISONERS ... *SLAVES* -- JUST LIKE YOUR OWN GRANDFATHER.

LET ME *FREE* THEM.

WHEN DID YOU GET SO GROWN UP, KID? WHEN DID YOU GET SO SMART?

A LOT HAS HAPPENED TO ME SINCE I LEFT HOME, JANEK. I'VE HAD SOME REALLY GOOD *TEACHERS* TO HELP ME GET THROUGH IT ALL...

...AND I HAD FRIENDS LIKE *YOU* WHEN I WAS GROWING UP.

TANK, THE ALLIANCE NEEDS GOOD MEN. YOU COULD MAKE A DIFFERENCE --

LUKE, I -- I'M *ALREADY* MAKING A DIFFERENCE. *HERE.* WITH THE *EMPIRE.*

IT'S NOT ALWAYS EASY, BUT WE'RE BRINGING ORDER ... DISCIPLINE ... TO WORLDS THAT NEVER --

SKYWALKER! IS THIS TUB READY FOR LIFT-OFF?

BIGGS?

YOU SAID HE DIED A HERO, SAVING YOU AT YAVIN FOUR.

TANK, BIGGS AND I WERE FIGHTING ON THE SIDE OF THE ALLIANCE. BIGGS DIED SO THAT I COULD DESTROY THE DEATH STAR.

HE AND I KNEW IT WAS THE RIGHT THING TO DO. I THOUGHT YOU WOULD, TOO.

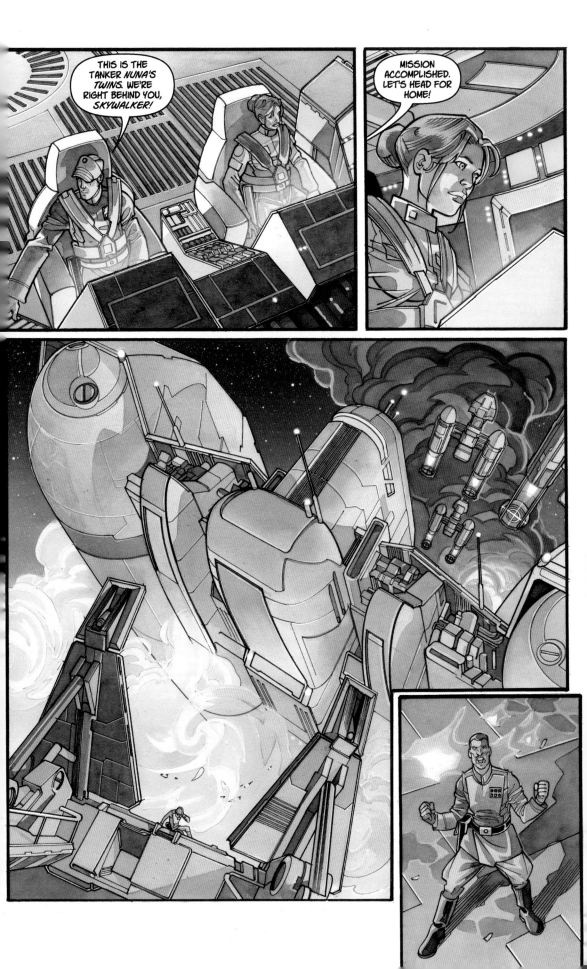

THE NEXT DAYS SEE A FLURRY OF ACTIVITY. REINFORCEMENTS ARRIVE, ALMOST BEFORE THEY'RE CALLED FOR, LEAVING SUNBER TO WONDER WHERE THEY WERE DURING THE ATTACK.

THE TWO INTELLIGENCE OFFICERS DISSUADE CAPTAIN ROSHUIR FROM BRINGING SUNBER UP ON CHARGES FOR THE ACTION HE TOOK AGAINST CLYNN. AS ALWAYS, THE LOGIC OF MILITARY JUSTICE CONFOUNDS SUNBER.

WITH BACTA TREATMENTS, HIS WOUND HEALS QUICKLY -- AS QUICKLY AS THE EMPIRE REPAIRS ITS BASE.

BUT THERE IS ANOTHER WOUND THAT REMAINS PAINFUL AND RAW. YET HE SPEAKS OF IT TO NO ONE. FOR NOW, IT IS HIS ALONE TO BEAR...

...HIS ALONE TO DWELL ON.

BIGGS. LUKE. IN A SINGLE DAY, JANEK SUNBER DISCOVERED THAT TWO OF HIS FRIENDS ARE GONE FOREVER. HIS EXPERIENCES HAVE TAUGHT HIM TO ACCEPT COMBAT LOSSES. BUT THIS IS THE FIRST TIME HE HAS EVER LOST ANYONE TO THE OTHER SIDE...

...AND THE FIRST TIME HE HAS EVER HAD TO CALL A FRIEND ... AN ENEMY.

THE END

STAR WARS®
TIMELINE OF GRAPHIC NOVELS FROM DARK HORSE!

OLD REPUBLIC ERA:
25,000—1000 YEARS BEFORE
STAR WARS: A NEW HOPE

Tales of the Jedi—
The Golden Age of the Sith
ISBN: 1-56971-229-8 $16.95

Tales of the Jedi—
The Fall of the Sith Empire
ISBN: 1-56971-320-0 $14.95

Tales of the Jedi—
Knights of the Old Republic
ISBN: 1-56971-020-1 $14.95

Tales of the Jedi—
The Freedon Nadd Uprising
ISBN: 1-56971-307-3 $5.95

Tales of the Jedi—
Dark Lords of the Sith
ISBN: 1-56971-095-3 $17.95

Tales of the Jedi—The Sith War
ISBN: 1-56971-173-9 $17.95

Tales of the Jedi—Redemption
ISBN: 1-56971-535-1 $14.95

Knights of the Old Republic
Volume 1—Commencement
ISBN: 1-59307-640-1 $18.95

Jedi vs. Sith
ISBN: 1-56971-649-8 $17.95

RISE OF THE EMPIRE ERA:
1000-0 YEARS BEFORE
STAR WARS: A NEW HOPE

The Stark Hyperspace War
ISBN: 1-56971-985-3 $12.95

Jedi Council—Acts of War
ISBN: 1-56971-539-4 $12.95

Prelude to Rebellion
ISBN: 1-56971-448-7 $14.95

Darth Maul
ISBN: 1-56971-542-4 $12.95

Episode I—The Phantom Menace
ISBN: 1-56971-359-6 $12.95

Episode I—
The Phantom Menace Adventures
ISBN: 1-56971-443-6 $12.95

Jango Fett
ISBN: 1-56971-623-4 $5.95

Zam Wesell
ISBN: 1-56971-624-2 $5.95

Jango Fett—Open Seasons
ISBN: 1-56971-671-4 $12.95

Outlander
ISBN: 1-56971-514-9 $14.95

Emissaries to Malastare
ISBN: 1-56971-545-9 $15.95

The Bounty Hunters
ISBN: 1-56971-467-3 $12.95

Twilight
ISBN: 1-56971-558-0 $12.95

The Hunt for Aurra Sing
ISBN: 1-56971-651-X $12.95

Darkness
ISBN: 1-56971-659-5 $12.95

Rite of Passage
ISBN: 1-59307-042-X $12.95

Honor and Duty
ISBN: 1-59307-546-4 $12.95

Episode II—Attack of the Clones
ISBN: 1-56971-609-9 $17.95

Clone Wars Volume 1—
The Defense of Kamino
ISBN: 1-56971-962-4 $14.95

Clone Wars Volume 2—
Victories and Sacrifices
ISBN: 1-56971-969-1 $14.95

Clone Wars Volume 3—
Last Stand on Jabiim
ISBN: 1-59307-006-3 $14.95

Clone Wars Volume 4—Light and Dark
ISBN: 1-59307-195-7 $16.95

Clone Wars Volume 5—The Best Blades
ISBN: 1-59307-273-2 $17.95

Clone Wars Volume 6—
On the Fields of Battle
ISBN: 1-59307-352-6 $17.95

Clone Wars Volume 7—
When They Were Brothers
ISBN: 1-59307-396-8 $17.95

Clone Wars Volume 8—
The Last Siege, The Final Truth
ISBN: 1-59307-482-4 $17.95

Clone Wars Volume 9—Endgame
ISBN: 1-59307-553-7 $17.95

Clone Wars Adventures Volume 1
ISBN: 1-59307-243-0 $6.95

Clone Wars Adventures Volume 2
ISBN: 1-59307-271-6 $6.95

Clone Wars Adventures Volume 3
ISBN: 1-59307-307-0 $6.95

Clone Wars Adventures Volume 4
ISBN: 1-59307-402-6 $6.95

Clone Wars Adventures Volume 5
ISBN: 1-59307-483-2 $6.95

Clone Wars Adventures Volume 6
ISBN: 1-59307-567-7 $6.95

Episode III—Revenge of the Sith
ISBN: 1-59307-309-7 $12.95

General Grievous
ISBN: 1-59307-442-5 $12.95

Droids—The Kalarba Adventures
ISBN: 1-56971-064-3 $17.95

Droids—Rebellion
ISBN: 1-56971-224-7 $14.95

Classic Star Wars—
Han Solo at Stars' End
ISBN: 1-56971-254-9 $6.95

Boba Fett—Enemy of the Empire
ISBN: 1-56971-407-X $12.95

Underworld—The Yavin Vassilika
ISBN: 1-56971-618-8 $15.95

Dark Forces—Soldier for the Empire
ISBN: 1-56971-348-0 $14.95

Empire Volume 1—Betrayal
ISBN: 1-56971-964-0 $12.95

Empire Volume 2—Darklighter
ISBN: 1-56971-975-6 $17.95

REBELLION ERA:
0-5 YEARS AFTER
STAR WARS: A NEW HOPE

A New Hope—The Special Edition
ISBN: 1-56971-213-1 $9.95

Empire Volume 3—
The Imperial Perspective
ISBN: 1-59307-128-0 $17.95

Empire Volume 4—
The Heart of the Rebellion
ISBN: 1-59307-308-9 $17.95

Empire Volume 5—Allies and Adversaries
ISBN: 1-59307-466-2 $14.95

Empire Volume 6—In the Footsteps
of Their Fathers
ISBN: 1-59307-627-4 $17.95

A Long Time Ago . . . Volume 1—
Doomworld
ISBN: 1-56971-754-0 $29.95

A Long Time Ago . . . Volume 2—
Dark Encounters
ISBN: 1-56971-785-0 $29.95

Classic Star Wars—
The Early Adventures
ISBN: 1-56971-178-X $19.95

Classic Star Wars Volume 1—
In Deadly Pursuit
ISBN: 1-56971-109-7 $16.95

Classic Star Wars Volume 2—
The Rebel Storm
ISBN: 1-56971-106-2 $16.95

Classic Star Wars Volume 3—
Escape to Hoth
ISBN: 1-56971-093-7 $16.95

Jabba the Hutt—The Art of the Deal
ISBN: 1-56971-310-3 $9.95

Vader's Quest
ISBN: 1-56971-415-0 $11.95

Splinter of the Mind's Eye
ISBN: 1-56971-223-9 $14.95

The Empire Strikes Back—
The Special Edition
ISBN: 1-56971-234-4 $9.95

A Long Time Ago . . . Volume 3—
Resurrection of Evil
ISBN: 1-56971-786-9 $29.95

A Long Time Ago . . . Volume 4—
Screams in the Void
ISBN: 1-56971-787-7 $29.95

A Long Time Ago . . . Volume 5—
Fool's Bounty
ISBN: 1-56971-906-3 $29.95

Battle of the Bounty Hunters
Pop-Up Book
ISBN: 1-56971-129-1 $17.95

Shadows of the Empire
ISBN: 1-56971-183-6 $17.95

Return of the Jedi—The Special Edition
ISBN: 1-56971-235-2 $9.95

A Long Time Ago . . . Volume 6—
Wookiee World
ISBN: 1-56971-907-1 $29.95

A Long Time Ago . . . Volume 7—
Far, Far Away
ISBN: 1-56971-908-X $29.95

Mara Jade—By the Emperor's Hand
ISBN: 1-56971-401-0 $15.95

Shadows of the Empire: Evolution
ISBN: 1-56971-441-X $14.95

NEW REPUBLIC ERA:
5-25 YEARS AFTER
STAR WARS: A NEW HOPE

Omnibus—X-Wing Rogue Squadron
Volume 1
ISBN: 1-59307-572-3 $24.95

Omnibus—X-Wing Rogue Squadron
Volume 2
ISBN: 1-59307-619-3 $24.95

X-Wing Rogue Squadron—
In the Empire's Service
ISBN: 1-56971-383-9 $12.95

X-Wing Rogue Squadron—
Blood and Honor
ISBN: 1-56971-387-1 $12.95

X-Wing Rogue Squadron—
Masquerade
ISBN: 1-56971-487-8 $12.95

X-Wing Rogue Squadron—
Mandatory Retirement
ISBN: 1-56971-492-4 $12.95

Dark Forces—Rebel Agent
ISBN: 1-56971-400-2 $14.95

Dark Forces—Jedi Knight
ISBN: 1-56971-433-9 $14.95

Heir to the Empire
ISBN: 1-56971-202-6 $19.95

Dark Force Rising
ISBN: 1-56971-269-7 $17.95

The Last Command
ISBN: 1-56971-378-2 $17.95

Boba Fett—
Death, Lies, and Treachery
ISBN: 1-56971-311-1 $12.95

Dark Empire
ISBN: 1-59307-039-X $16.95

Dark Empire II
ISBN: 1-59307-526-X $19.95

Empire's End
ISBN: 1-56971-306-5 $5.95

Crimson Empire
ISBN: 1-56971-355-3 $17.95

Crimson Empire II: Council of Blood
ISBN: 1-56971-410-X $17.95

Jedi Academy: Leviathan
ISBN: 1-56971-456-8 $11.95

Union
ISBN: 1-56971-464-9 $12.95

NEW JEDI ORDER ERA:
25+ YEARS AFTER
STAR WARS: A NEW HOPE

Chewbacca
ISBN: 1-56971-515-7 $12.95

INFINITIES:
DOES NOT APPLY TO TIMELINE

Infinites: A New Hope
ISBN: 1-56971-648-X $12.95

Infinities: The Empire Strikes Back
ISBN: 1-56971-904-7 $12.95

Infinities: Return of the Jedi
ISBN: 1-59307-206-6 $12.95

Star Wars Tales Volume 1
ISBN: 1-56971-619-6 $19.95

Star Wars Tales Volume 2
ISBN: 1-56971-757-5 $19.95

Star Wars Tales Volume 3
ISBN: 1-56971-836-9 $19.95

Star Wars Tales Volume 4
ISBN: 1-56971-989-6 $19.95

Star Wars Tales Volume 5
ISBN: 1-59307-286-4 $19.95

Star Wars Tales Volume 6
ISBN: 1-59307-447-6 $19.95

Tag & Bink Were Here
ISBN: 1-59307-641-X $14.95

FOR MORE INFORMATION ABOUT THESE BOOKS VISIT DARKHORSE.COM!

AVAILABLE AT YOUR LOCAL COMICS SHOP OR BOOKSTORE
To find a comics shop in your area, call 1-888-266-4226. For more information or to order direct, visit darkhorse.com or call 1-800-862-0052 Mon.–Fri. 9 A.M. to 5 P.M. Pacific Time. *Prices and availability subject to change without notice.

STAR WARS ©2006 Lucasfilm Ltd. & ™. (BL8009)